What do you do if it's raining and you're confined to barracks?

For a start you can steep yourself in cowboy lore and ride into the Wild West with quizzes and crosswords ... or organize a bears' picnic and bake really yummy goodies ... or learn all the secrets of a secret agent and become a master spy ... or get involved in crazy history mysteries – to mention just a few of the excitements in *Under Cover*, all accompanied with zany illustrations by Arthur Robins.

If you're about eight or nine or ten, you'll find something funny to read, something original to make or play, and something absorbing to do in every chapter.

UNDERCOVER
DEBORAH JARVIS

AN INDOOR
ADVENTURE BOOK

ILLUSTRATED
BY ARTHUR ROBINS

COLLINS LIONS

To Pinky and Beano
for all the wet afternoons
they put up with me

The Editors gratefully acknowledge permission to
reprint copyright material from *Toad of Toad Hall*
by A. A. Milne to Curtis Brown Ltd, London, on
behalf of the Estates of Kenneth Grahame and A. A.
Milne and to Charles Scribner's Sons, copyright 1929.

First published in Lions 1975
by William Collins Sons and Co Ltd
14 St James's Place, London SW1

© Deborah Jarvis 1975
© Illustrations Arthur Robins 1975

Printed in Great Britain
by William Collins Sons and Co Ltd, Glasgow

INSIDE

CUSTER'S LAST STAND
defeated by
Sitting Bull and
his warriors.

Sioux In[dians]
led by Craz[y]

FT. LARAMIE

SACRAMENTO

● SALT LAKE
CITY

Union
Pacific
Railway
1st east-west railway

GOLDRUSH

SAN FRANCISCO

Wells Fargo

PONY EXPRE[SS]
delivered lett[ers]
EAST to West in

Bear Rebellion Flag
designed when California
Settlers rebelled against
Mexicans.

WELLS FARGO EXPRESS
largest stage coach
service in the West

Texas Longhorns
breed of very
long-haired cattle
almost extinct
now

Wild B[ill]
"fastest d[raw]
Sheriff
ABILEN[E]

ROCKY
MOUNTAINS

TEX[AS]
(Lone St[ar]

APACHE INDIANS
led by Geronimo
fierce scalp-hunters

S[anta Fe?]
oldes[t]
city in

RIO GRANDE

6

THE WILD WEST

Fasten your seat-belts. You are about to take a flying trip back into the past. It lasts for five minutes only and during that time you must try and see as much of the Wild West as you can. Then turn over and tackle the Cowboy Quiz!

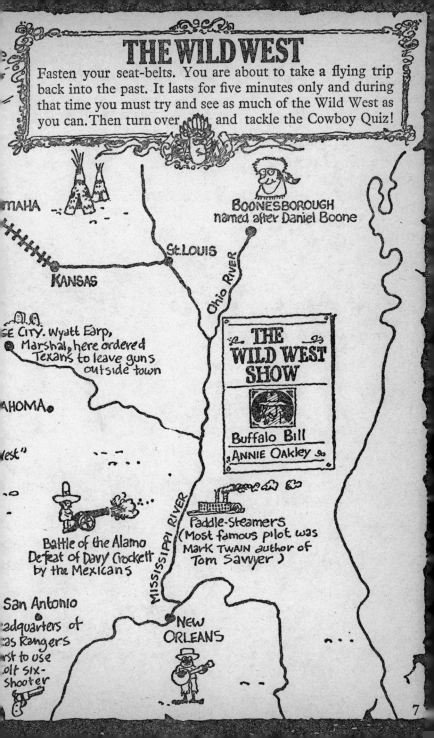

MAHA

KANSAS

SE CITY. Wyatt Earp, Marshal, here ordered Texans to leave guns outside town

AHOMA

est"

BOONESBOROUGH named after Daniel Boone

St.LOUIS

Ohio RIVER

THE WILD WEST SHOW

Buffalo Bill

ANNIE OAKLEY

Battle of the Alamo Defeat of Davy Crockett by the Mexicans

MISSISSIPPI RIVER

Paddle-Steamers (Most famous pilot was Mark Twain author of Tom Sawyer)

San Antonio adquarters of as Rangers rst to use olt Six-Shooter

NEW ORLEANS

COWBOY QUIZ

How quickly can you lasso the right answers to this Cowboy Quiz?
Have a friend time you or time yourself but remember – don't look back.

1. On a map, the Union Pacific would look like this

   a) ┼┼┼┼┼┼
   b) VVVV
   c) – – – – –

2. Davy Crockett was defeated by

   a) the rush for gold
   b) the Mexicans
   c) a horde of raccoons chasing his hat
   d) the Indians

3. Which of the following people were *not* in the Wild West Show

   a) Dale Evans
   b) The Lone Ranger
   c) Annie Oakley
   d) Pocahontas

4. The Colt looked like this

   a) (rifle)
   b) (revolver)
   c) (cannon)

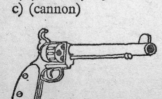

5. The Indians in Texas who loved scalps best and palefaces least were the

a) Bald Ones
b) Apaches
c) Sioux

6. Colonel Custer's last battle went down in history as Custer's

a) Last Sitting
b) Drastic Plan
c) Blasted Hand
d) Last Stand
e) Final Sit-Down

7. At this momentous event he was defeated by Chief

a) Want 'em White Man
b) Kicking Horse
c) Jumping Cow
d) Sitting Bull

8. The Wells Fargo Company was in business to

a) sell wells which had not far to go
b) run stagecoaches
c) 'deliver the goods' – its real name was Wells Cargo

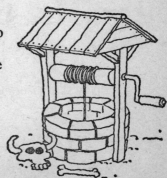

9

9. Paddle-steamers operated up and down the

    a) Rio Grande
    b) Thames
    c) Rocky Mountains
    d) Mississippi

10. A famous paddle-steamer pilot was

    a) Tom Sawyer
    b) Mary Poppins
    c) Mark Twain
    d) Big Ben

MAKE YOUR MARK

Every spring the cowboys ride out to the herd and mark all the young calves to show that they belong to a certain owner Each ranch has its own brand that cannot be confused with any other.

Here are a few examples to give you an idea of what they look like:

lazy S   lone star   flying O   crazy M   rocking P

Can you design brands for these ranches?

Circle T   Big Valley   Pine Top   Triple R   OK Corral

Why not design your own personal brand to use on letters, notes, and secret messages. You will need:
half a potato   pen   knife   paper   ink and brush

1. Work out your brand design on paper first. The simpler it is, the easier it will be to make.
2. With a pen, draw your final design on the flat half of the potato.
3. Then carefully cut away all the potato from the outside and inside of your design so that when you have finished, the lines of the brand stand out above the rest.
4. Place the sheet of paper which you are brand-stamping on a flat surface. With a brush, ink the raised part of your design.
5. Before the ink dries, turn the stamp over quickly and 'brand' the paper. Re-ink for each 'branding'.

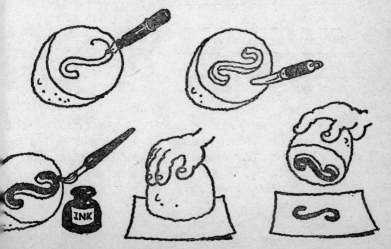

ON THE WARPATH

The Indians were called redskins, not because their skins actually were red, but because they painted them that colour with berry juice or vegetable dyes.

If you would like to be a redskin, a blueskin, or even a rainbowskin, mix up your own pot of warpaint.

Warpaint

1. Gather together different coloured fresh fruits and vegetables. These ones make particularly good colours:

strawberries	bright red
raspberries	blue-red
cherries	dark-red
tomatoes	medium red
(although paste is	
better)	
blackcurrants	blue
peas	green

(Beware of using most tinned fruits or vegetables which have artificial colouring and will not work as warpaint.)
2. Mash up the fruit until it makes a smooth paste. (You do not need much fruit, only about 1–2 ounces of each.)
3. Then with fingers or brush apply it to your face in war-like designs.

To get you started here are a few warpaint patterns:

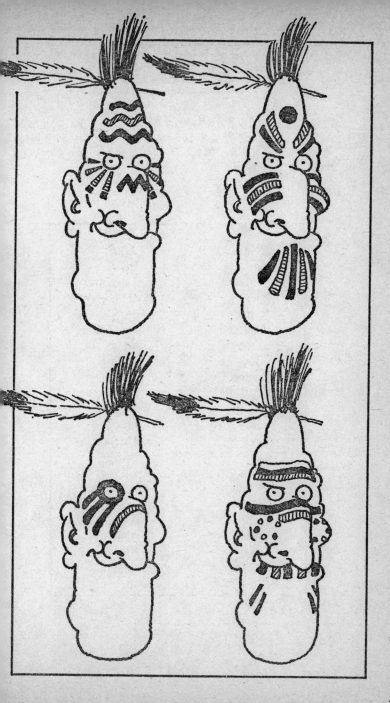

13

ROUND-UP

A large part of a cowboy's time is spent rounding up strays. Try your hand at the ones below and see if you can round up each word with its matching mate.

steamer	Mark
wam	baked
Buffalo	Laramie
bronco	schooner
Ranger	wig
shooter	star state
coach	wow
pow	Bill
Dodge	Boones
flap	buster
prairie	Texas
borough	hole
Rocky	Horse
lone	paddle
beans	City
cattle	six
Grande	jacks
water	Mountains
Fort	rustler
Crazy	Rio
Twain	stage

CHUCK WAGON

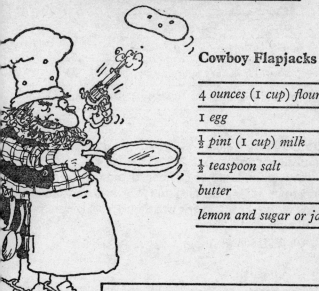

Cowboy Flapjacks

4 ounces (1 cup) flour
1 egg
½ pint (1 cup) milk
½ teaspoon salt
butter
lemon and sugar or jam

1. Put flour and salt through sieve into large bowl.
2. Add egg and blend in well.
3. Pour in milk a little at a time and stir until mixture is smooth.
4. Melt enough butter in frying pan to cover the bottom and heat until steaming.
5. Pour just enough batter in pan to cover the bottom and cook until underside is golden brown.
6. Then flip over (brave cooks can flip into the air) and cook the second side until brown.
7. Add your favourite filling – jam or lemon and sugar.
8. Flip flapjack on to plate and dig in!

Broncobuster Beans

I *large can baked beans*
2 *teaspoons brown sugar*
I *pinch mustard*
6 *frankfurter sausages*
optional: I *teaspoon molasses or black treacle*

1. Cut up frankfurter sausages, put in medium-sized saucepan, and heat until boiling.
2. Pour water off and add can of baked beans.
3. Stir in brown sugar, mustard and molasses and mix well.
4. Put back on the heat and stir occasionally to keep mixture from sticking.
5. Serve when piping hot.

Note to Cowboys:
Although it is traditional for cowboys to eat cross-legged on the ground and not use their hands to get up or sit down, trying this first with a full plate in your hands and without practice could have disastrous consequences!

COWBOY TALK

Cowboys have a 'lingo' all of their own, words that outsiders often have difficulty understanding. How well do you think you would fare if thrown in the midst of cowboy country?

1. If someone pointed out Sitting Bull to you, you would:

   a) exclaim, 'Doesn't that bull ever stand up?'
   b) run in the opposite direction
   c) sit down with him

2. If a long tall Texan said to you, 'Let's have a show-down', you would:

   a) take him to the show down the street
   b) go for your gun
   c) presume he means 'slow-down' and leave school early

3. If you overheard someone talking about 'little dogies', you would know they were talking about:

   a) small-size hot dogs
   b) puppies
   c) young cattle

4. Calling someone 'mean and ornery' means they are:

   a) mean but perfectly ordinary
   b) mean with big horns
   c) mean and nasty

5. If you were asked to help yourself to 'Shivering Liz', you would reach for:

   a) the girl shivering at the end of the table
   b) the jelly dessert
   c) a cold lizard

6. If you were given a job as cowpuncher, you would have

   a) punch cows all day long
   b) ride cows and punch people
   c) work with cows on horseback

7. You would expect a 'critter' to be:

   a) a creature with four legs
   b) a cross between a croak and a twitter
   c) a corn fritter

8. A 'varmint' is:

   a) a real rascal
   b) an after-dinner mint
   c) a worm

9. Cowboys talking about a 'nice spread' would mean:

   a) a nice spread eagle
   b) a jam with no lumps
   c) a good-sized ranch

10. If the cowboys started to sing, 'Home, home on the . . .' the next word would be:

   a) racecourse   c) farm
   b) horse   d) ranch
                      e) range

WANTED:ALIVE

WANTED
BILLY THE KID

FOR CATTLE RUSTLING

REWARD
$500

The sheriff's office used to be full of posters offering rewards for the capture – dead or alive – of certain outlaws. You can make the same sort of poster to use as an invitation, birthday present or card for a friend (leaving out the 'dead' part if you want to keep him as a friend).

Here is how to do it:

1. Get a large piece of cardboard and fill it in like this:
2. Glue a picture of your friend in the centre space. If you do not have one of him or her, find a picture in a colour magazine that looks vaguely like him and glue it into the space instead. Then cut out a picture of a hat (it does not have to be a cowboy one and the funnier the better) and glue it on as well. Draw a moustache or bushy eyebrows to make it look authentic.
3. Underneath write:

   a) if it is an invitation: For tea next Tuesday at 3.00
   Reward – toast and marmalade

   b) if it is his birthday: For his ...th birthday
   Reward – birthday cake and presents

   c) if it is just for fun: For a pow-wow with Sitting Bull (or put your name instead)

COWBOY CROSSWORD

Across

1. a man who tames bucking broncos
8. an Indian tribe has .... chief and many warriors
9. saddle, boots, hat and bedroll make up a cowboy.........
10. a name given to the British soldiers because of their red uniforms
11. Davy Crockett was beaten at the ....
14. Daniel Boone wore a hat with a ....
16. Indians shot with a .... and arrow
17. a marshal stands for .... and order
18. the oldest capital city in the U.S. is Santa .... (rhymes with hay)
19. soldiers shot through .... in the fort walls
23. early settlers kept their tobacco in a .... (rhymes with grouch)
26. the Wells Fargo Express was the biggest......... service in the West

28. How would you spell this brand: L
29. cowboys barbecue these over an open fire
31. the first east-west mail service was the Pony ....
32. the Marshal of Dodge City was Wyatt ....
33. a Colt is a .... -shooter
34. answering your commanding officer, you would say 'Yes .... !'

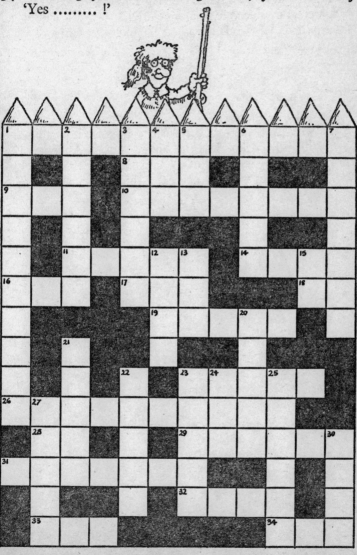

Down

1. a cowboy's favourite dish
2. another word for bandit
3. an enclosure that horses are kept in
4. each cattle town had ...... general store
5. a cowboy sleeps in a ...... -roll
6. the man who rode ahead on the look-out for trouble
7. a cattle thief

12.

13. a wise bird, the rancher's friend because it eats mice
15. Wild Bill Hickok was the Sher.....f of Abilene
20. a white flag is a sign of ...... (rhymes with spruce)
21. the Apaches were great ......-hunters

22.

23. a band of men sent out to catch an outlaw
24. for breakfast, cowboys eat porridge, made from ...... meal
25. the cowboys who stay on the bucking broncos are the rodeo ......
27. the .... Rangers were the first to use the Colt revolver

30.

RHYMES WITHOUT REASON

Do you ever get your mords in a wuddle or rather, your words in a muddle? Say what a feckle fillow when you mean what a fickle fellow, or chilly sap instead of silly chap, porkshire yudding for yorkshire pudding?

Why can't words behave themselves and do as they are told? They are always saying the wrong thing and then disappearing just when you need them. And as for their spelling . . .

This chapter is all about word muddles and how to get the better of them. It shows you how to become an expert muddler yourself by mastering the art of Un-muddle, Re-muddle and Muddle Along.

Here are some exasperating examples of words misbehaving in a set of unreasonable rhymes. Their lines have been leaping about quite out of control, so that now they are left with no rhyme and no reason. As a warm-up for future un-muddling, can you unravel them and put the rhymes back in their proper order?

Tom, Tom, the piper's son
Hey, diddle, diddle,
Stole a pig and away he run,
The cat and the fiddle
The little dog laughed
To see such sport.

The pig was eat
And the dish ran away with the spoon;
The cow jumped over the moon
And Tom went howling down the street.

The Queen was in the parlour
She made some tarts
The Queen of Hearts
All on a summer's day.

The King was in the Counting-House
Hanging out the clothes,
When down came a blackbird
And took them clear away.

The maid was in the garden
Eating bread and honey,
The Knave of Hearts
Counting out his money,
He stole those tarts
And pecked off her nose.

t's raining, it's pouring
Dr Foster went to Gloucester
He went to bed with a cold in his head
And never went there again.

The old man is snoring
In a shower of rain
He stepped in a puddle right up to his middle
And didn't wake up until morning.

Pussy cat, pussy cat, where have you been?
Upstairs and downstairs
And in my lady's chamber
Whither shall I wander.

I've been to London to look at the Queen
There I met an old man
Who would not say his prayers
Goosey, goosey gander.

Pussy cat, pussy cat, what did you there?
I frightened a little mouse under her chair,
I took him by the left leg
And threw him down the stairs.

Wee Willie Winkie runs through the town,
One shoe off and one shoe on,
Upstairs and downstairs, in his nightgown
Rapping at the window, crying through the lock.

Diddle, diddle, dumpling, my son John
Are the children in their beds?
For now it's eight o'clock,
Diddle, diddle, dumpling, my son John
Went to bed with his trousers on.

It is not just rhymes that get in a muddle. As you will discover later on, tales get in a twist as well. You can see how
easily this happens by doing a little muddling yourself.

PUZZLING PICTURES

You will need:

old comics   heavy cardboard   glue   scissors   penc

1. Take a whole page (or half, depending on how big the pa
   is) of a comic and glue it to a piece of cardboard.
2. With a pencil, draw interlocking pieces like a jigsaw.
3. With your scissors, cut along the lines you have ju
   drawn so that you are left with a pile of jigsaw pieces.

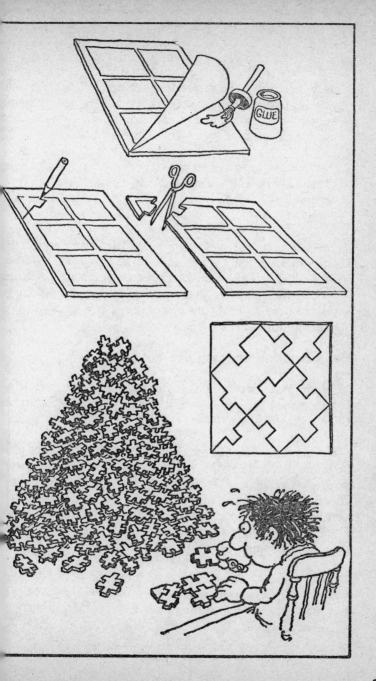

It is up to you to decide what to do next.
You can:

have a friend make a puzzling picture at the same time
you are making yours. When they are both cut out, swap
puzzles and have a race to see who can put theirs back
together again first.

give the pieces to a member of your family and time him
to see how quickly he can piece it together. Have a com
petition to see who is the fastest 'picture puzzler' in your
family.

post the pieces in an envelope to a friend and ask him t
write or ring you back as soon as he has put it together
Make him tell you the punchline or number of differen
sections in the comic, just to prove he has really done it
(He could also post you one at the same time you post
yours and make it a race.)

For advanced unscramblers:

Why not make two puzzles at the same time, mix the piece
together and then see how fast you or your friends can pu
them together again.

Make a different sort of puzzling picture by cutting out par
of different comic strips and pasting them in a patchwor
design on cardboard. Then you can either present it to
friend as it is and ask him to name all the different comic
you have included, or make it into a jigsaw puzzle. If yo
leave it together, you can varnish and frame it or use it t
cover a wastepaper basket.

P.S. If you haven't any old comics around the house, yo
can use page advertisements out of colour magazines. Yo
can make puzzles out of them and ask your friends to gue.
what they advertise!

HISTORY MYSTERIES

For those who find history rather a mystery, this chapter is really for you. You are about to discover a most unusual account: A Case of Mysterious History. The dates are all there, the names ring a bell, but the facts are a trifle confused. It is up to you now to pull the facts from the fiction. By reading these pages and spotting the errors, you will sort out the mystery and rescue the history.

Willy-Nilly

Long ago – in a country not far (enough) from here – there lived a King called Willy-Nilly who was bored.

I'm bored

① Frankly, he'd had it with hunting, fishing, jesting at court and all that.

JOKES

What he wanted was a little fun or better still, big fun. One day he said to his men (all called Norman) ② 'Allo, Allo. Vot about a qweek conquer across ze Channel?'

Norman!

This was greeted by a great round of applause by All the Kings Men, who were half-packed by the time he had finished speaking.

HASTINGS

Meanwhile – across this very channel a young Chap by the name of Earl Hair-Oiled *3) heard (via the grape wine) that Willy-Nilly was on his way to England to give him a good thrashing.

What!

With frightening speed, he raced his army down to the coast to tell that fellow where he couldn't get off.

But *alas*, he wasn't quick enough. Willy-Nilly was half way through a cream cake by the time he ran into Hair-Oiled.

Annoyed at Hair-Oiled for interrupting his tea, Willy-Nilly was determined to have his cake and eat it too.

He gave the order for his men to shoot their crumpets and Jam rolls into the air so that they came down like a shower of tea on the unsuspecting heads of the enemy.

This left the English with their mouths open, waiting for a tea cake to drop in.

They ate on obstinately until Willy-Nilly, getting hungry by now, finally lost patience and told his men to pretend to run away.

When the English gave chase he beat them soundly and sent most of them home without supper.

31

Just to show how pleased he was with the whole situation, Willy-Nilly changed his name to ....(4) and became King of England on Christmas Day 1066.

Just what I wanted

He then sent his men around the countryside, making a nuisance of themselves by asking everyone embarrassing questions and writing all the answers down in a large book.

This made everyone so miserable that it has been referred to ever since as The Gloomsday Book.

Quiz

1. Being *frank*, he could only have been from ....
2. If all his men were called Norman, this must have been The .... Conquest.
3. Olde English spelling. How would his name be written today?
4. If his last name was The Conqueror, what was his first?
5. Some historians persist in calling this book by another name. What is it?

Challenges

1. If you were Willy-Nilly, off to a quick conquer, which of the following provisions would you take with you?

crossbows	tents	raincoats
arrows	sleeping-bags	tanks
gunshot	tables	crumpets
winter woollies	chairs	cheese
tea	wellingtons	tobacco

guns
blankets
turnips
swords
horses
daggers
umbrellas
pillows
cows
wine
milk
toast and jam

2. This is a postcard sent by Willy-Nilly to his mother after he had been crowned King of England. Can you fill it in for him?

Post Card	
From:	**To:** Queen W. Nilly Centre Court France

U—B

King John I

King John I was not a bad king, he was the Worst. Greedy right from the start, he could not <u>wait</u> to become King...

His brother Richard the Lemon Tart (1) was away at the Crusades for such a long time that John got fed up and tried to seize the crown himself.

But he was so big headed that the crown didn't fit, and he was forced to go without cream and sweets for many months.

When at last he got the crown on, he cried, 'Jam first!' and tucked into a huge cream tea, going down in history as King Jam the First.

As the first Jam King, he went about insisting that the Right of Kings was divine and putting his sticky fingers into other people's business.

He paid no attention to his subjects which was not a good thing as one of them, a certain Robin Pud (2) paid rather a lot of attention to him and really got his gold.

expert mathematician, Mr. R. Pud. ...ent around reducing halves to ...alf naughts when ever possible.

He and his Feathered Friends refused to play fair and beat John and his men with their hands tied.

...ohn, in a jam again, went ...f conquering the Welsh, ...e Scots and anyone else ...the vicinity. ...e then got on his ...gh horse and ...ommanded ...e barons to ...oss the ...annel & ...ght ...ance

The barons had no intention of getting their feet wet and refused straight off.

John was therefore forced to set off with an army of hired hands.

FOR HIRE

...t only did John lose many ...these hands but he was ...undly de-feeted as well!

Meanwhile at home the barons, though well-manored, were not to be feuded with and decided to teach John a lesson (or two).

On a hillside near Runny Mead (3) in 1215, they made John sign an enormous document which said that Might was not Right and that he was to stop lording it over them.

This document has been known ever since as the The Magnanamous Charter (4) since the barons were generous enough to give John the choice of either signing it or having his head cut off.

Quiz

1. This does not sound quite right. Do you think he could have been a peach pie instead? Jot down all the clues to his identity here.
2. If you think Robin Pud could have had another name, please say so.
3. This is:
   a) an old Cornish drink   b) a town near Windsor
   c) a river called Mead

4. The Latin name for this document was:
   a) Maggy Carter   b) Magnum Cartum   c) Magna Carta

Challenges

1. By a stroke of good luck, the ancient recipe for Robin Pudding (named after Robin Pud) has been discovered. Unfortunately it is still written in Olde English and with ingredients which regrettably are no longer available. Can you translate the recipe and guess what its name is today?

Robin Pudding

1. Take a roll from Friar's Tuck.
2. Shoot into bite-size pieces and hurl into a wooden bowl (preferably empty).
3. Throw in a handful of the Sheriff of Nottingham's men. (Remove outer layers and wash thoroughly first.)
4. Mix well, or if necessary beat, until the Sheriff's men have blended in.
5. Extract ten cherries – about the shade of Will Scarlet – from a nearby tree (or if possible the Sheriff's larder) and stir in.
6. Into this add a dash of wild deer and a pinch of Maid

Marion.

7. Follow by a bull's eye of sugar and a quarter-quiver full of custard.
8. Douse the mixture in mead. (Little John is not to sample it first.)
9. Rob a rich abbot of his double cream and after a good thrashing, fling across the top of the mixture.
10. Leave the mixture until it turns a pleasant shade of green, then serve at once to merry men.

P.S. You will find the modern name for this recipe, but only if you are stumped, in the first letters of steps 3, 5, 6, 7, 9 and 10. Straighten them out for the final delight.

2. On a large piece of cardboard make a Magnanamous Charter, showing how generous you are, for one of your friends. To make it look more authentic, run the edges with a pencil or a piece of charcoal; then put it in a warm oven for a few minutes to make it dry and crinkly.

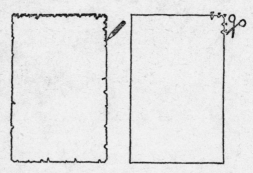

Magnanamous Charter

I, ..., on the ...... day of the month of the year ...., do hereby promise the honourable ....
that I will .... from this time forward and do solemnly swear to abide by this charter as long as I shall live.

Signed,

King James I

got off to a good start as king of England by becoming king of Scotland first.

He was there-fore known to eat rock (made in Edinburgh) and loved a good fling.

Once crowned, he put his considerable weight behind the Church of England and suggested that all those who had not joined would kindly do so immediately.

BOOM!
BOOM!
BOOM!

There were a number of people who did not take this at all kindly and insisted on going their own puritanical way.

One group in particular (mainly fathers) (1) were compelled to go on a pilgrimage across the Atlantic in a ship called 'May flower' or 'May Not' (2)...

... and arranged for an annual holiday called Thanksgiving to be held in the colonies.

39

But James still did not give up and persecuted these independents until they were ready to explode.

On November 5, 1605, a man called Sly Fox (3) tried to make way for a new parliament by blowing up the present one.

His attempt was not successful, but the event is still celebrated today as 'Buy Socks Day' (4).

DRATS! I've left my matches at home! *☆

STAND WELL BACK
BEST GUN POWER

Quiz

1. Three guesses as to what this group was called.
2. There seems to be some confusion about the name of this ship. Which do you think is the right one?
3. This was only a disguise. What was his real name?
4. If it was not 'Buy Socks Day', what was it?

Challenge

All our holidays have been around for a very long time. Why don't we dream up some new ones? It would be rather fun to have an Animal Day, celebrated by a National Animal Parade, or a Football Day, when everything closed down to watch or play football, or a Walking Day, giving a holiday to buses, cars, trains and planes.

Organize a New Holiday Competition among your friends with a prize of a 'New Holiday' for two. Why don't you be the first to enter?

OFFICIAL ENTRY FORM FOR NEW HOLIDAYS

I think we should have a new holiday called..............
to take place on .... for .... day(s).
It would be in honour of .... and
.......................would have the day off.

This holiday would be very much like

...St. Patrick's Day
...Christmas
...Hallowe'en
...Valentine's Day
...Easter

SCHOOL HOLIDAYS
MON ... Animal Day
TUE ... Football Day
WED ... SAUSAGE DAY
THUR... TELEVISION D/
FRI ... VISITING DAY
NOTE: TO BE REPEATED
EVERY OTHER WEEK

Everyone would/would not wear buttons like this: (fill in your own design)

carry banners like this: (another design here)

costumes like this would/would not be worn: (draw a small picture here)

The dish of the day
would be

..pancakes
..spaghetti
..baked beans
..chocolate cake
..fish and chips
..none of these, instead ....

We would drink the
holiday's health with

..hot chocolate
..orange squash
..tea
..lemonade
..coca-cola

The day's festivities
would include

..Morris dancing
..fireworks
..parties
..bonfires
..giving presents
..singing
..staying out late
..getting up early
..playing sports

This holiday would
come into effect

..immediately
..when school term st:
..in ten years when
  I start working

Treasure Hunt

All those who would like to sail for the Spanish Main right now in search of treasure, say 'Aye!' (but not too loudly, the secret agents in Chapter 7 might be listening). If you're ready, find a Jolly Roger (or any jolly friend) and let's go!

To get started, you need a ship and a good map. After that, it's as easy as 1–2–3.

The ship is the easiest to track down and can be found amongst your own treasure. A penny piece (or a ha'penny, depending on your wealth at that moment) decorated with your colours or a special design glued or sello-taped to the top.

Next the map. If you haven't one handy, draw a map on a large piece of cardboard, using the one on the next page as a model. (Hint: if you trace the outline of a coin, all the circles will come out the same size.) To make the map brighter and more appealing to your crew, paint, pencil, or crayon in the circles with different colours.

Once this is done, you can concentrate on the next step which is *getting* there. On p. 46 you will find a set of Action cards which give you all the directions to Treasure Island. (Don't lose these or you *will* be lost!) Cut out twenty-four pieces of cardboard about the size of playing cards and trace the design and instructions of the models on p. 46 on to each card. Then stack them up into an 'Action Pack' and put to one side of the map.

But you are still not ready to go until you've chosen the Captains. Cut out three more cards and draw the face and name of a different Captain (shown on p. 48) on each one. (If there are more than three players, you can expand the game by enlarging the board and making more Captain cards.) Turn them over and deal one card to each pirate joining in the hunt. The card you are dealt tells you which Captain you will be for the hunt.

Before setting sail, there are three things you must do:
1. put three treasure chests (sugar lumps) on Smuggler's Cove
2. give each Captain four treasure chests (sugar lumps again)
3. and two pistols (matchsticks)

Once the map, cards, treasure and weapons are organized prepare to cast off. But first all pirates are obliged to read and obey, the Treasure Hunt Rules.

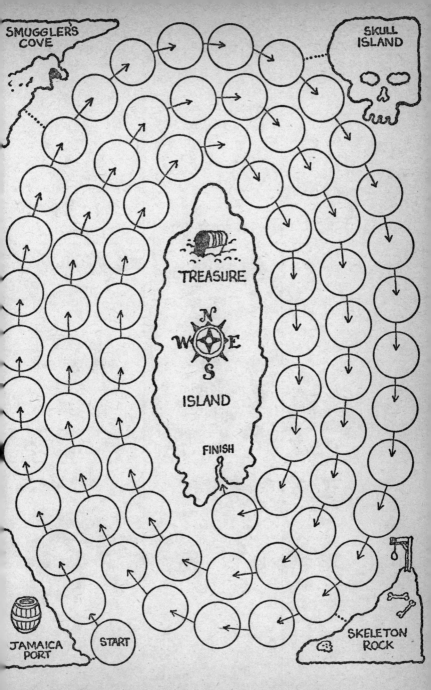

SMUGGLERS COVE

SKULL ISLAND

TREASURE

N
W E
S

ISLAND

FINISH

JAMAICA PORT

START

SKELETON ROCK

45

Drop Anchor — Miss 1 Turn

Man Overboard — Back 2 spaces

Ship Ahoy! — Move 2 spaces forward

Hoist the Jolly Roger — Advance 1 space

Blackbeard — Hand over 1 treasure chest

Stowaway — Return to Jamaica

Stand & Deliver — Give 1 treasure chest to Cap'n Kidd

Revenue Cutter — Stay where you are

Land~oh? — Advance 4 spaces

46

Move back 3 spaces

or Walk the Plank

Sailor Marooned

Fetch him from Skeleton Rock

Mutiny!

Back 1 space

Spin a yarn

Sail ahead 3 spaces

Shiver my Timbers it's Capn Morgan

Give him 1 treasure Chest

Clear Sailing

Overtake ship closest to you

Caught Smuggling

Back 2 spaces

Enemy Landing Party

Retreat 3 spaces

Dig up Buried Treasure

Pick up 1 treasure chest from Smugglers Cove

Throw all
Weapons
Overboard
Captain's Orders!

Rough
Seas
Seek Shelter
In Skull Island

Quarrels,
among the
Crew
2 Pistols Lost

All hands
on Deck
Move forward
3 spaces

Reef ahead
Move 1 space
to starboard (right)

Swab the
Decks
Take another turn

Blackbeard

Captain Kidd

Captain Morgan

Treasure Hunt Rules

All the ships must start together at the Jamaica Port.

Captain Morgan (as the oldest seadog) always sails first and draws the top card of the Action Pack. He must then move his ship according to the instructions marked on the card. Captain Kidd draws next, then Blackbeard and so on throughout the hunt.

No ship, regardless of winds, may move without turning up a card from the Action Pack. Only one card may be turned up at a time, unless the card itself says otherwise. When ships are ordered to a certain destination they must land on the circle to which it is connected with a dotted line.

The Captains must keep their weapons and treasure with them at all times. The first ship to reach Treasure Island gets the treasure, which is worth ten points, but must subtract two points for each missing pistol. Then he tallies up his score adding three points for each treasure chest in his possession.

All ships must dock at Treasure Island and the Captains tally up their scores before the winner is proclaimed. The Captain with the highest score wins!

TALES WITH A TWIST

The tales in this chapter are in a terrible muddle. Can you sort them out and put the words back in their original order? One way of doing this is by experimenting with the beginnings and endings of words. You could try changing the ending of one word with the ending of another so that the ugly sisters would become the sisty uglers; or the first letters of two words could be switched so that a pound rumpkin becomes a round pumpkin. Once you have worked them all out, try reading the stories out loud to someone else and see if they can untangle the twists.

The Pee Little Thrigs

Once upon a time, a tong lime ago, there lived an old sink pow with pee little thrigs. As she was a very poor old sow and didn't have enough foney to meed them, she sent them out to fork their seetunes.

The prist little figgy set off in a hurry to see what he could find. No sooner had he heft the louse than he met a munny old fan with a strundle of baw.

'Old man,' he said, 'Give me that straw so I can hake a mouse.'

The munny old fan was too frightened of the piggle litty to say no and gave him all his straw in one swell foop. Soon the prist little figgy was hard at work haking his mouse and had just finished it when along came a wean old molf who danged at the boor:

'Piggle-litty, piggle-litty, let me in.'

But the prist little figgy wasn't fooled and said,

'No, no, not by the chair of my hinny, chin, chin.'

But the wean old molf wouldn't give up and said,
'I'll huff and I'll puff and I'll blouse your how in.'

So he huffed and he puffed and he hew the blouse in and
gobbled the pirst little figgy up in two gig bulps.

Wheanmile, the second litty piggle was on his way to
fording his fintune and met an old man with a stundle of
bicks.

'Please, sir,' he said, 'give me that bund of stickles so that
I can build a house.'

The man did so and the litty piggle built a beauti-
houseful out of sticks. But no sooner had he put the stast lick
in place when who should come along but that wean old
nolf.

'Litty piggle, litty piggle, do let me come in.'

'Hot by the nair of my chinny, chin, chin,' said the litty
piggle.

'Then I'll huff and I'll puff and I'll how your blouse in,'
replied the wolf.

So he huffed and he puffed and he puffed and he huffed

and soon he whew the hole blouse in and ate up the litt
piggle, turly cail and all.

But at that moy verment, the lird pittle thiggy met a ma
carrying a broad of licks.

'Sind kir,' said he, 'could you give me brose thicks so
can build a house?'

The man gave him the bricks and in no time at all, th
house was built. Some lime tater, the wolf appeared
hooking very lungry and saying,

'Pittle-lig, pittle-lig, let me come in.'

But the lird pittle thiggy was smuch moo tart and sai

'Oh no, you wocked old wilf, not by the hairy of my chin
chin, chin.'

So the wolf huffed and he puffed and he puffed and h
huffed but he couldn't how that douse blown.

The wolf became very angry and thought to himself

'I must lap that pittle triggy.'

So he said, 'There are some nit-face turnips in Barme
Frown's field. Will you go with me to get some at cli
o'sock tomorning morrow, pittle-lig?'

'Yes, I will,' replied the litty piggle. But he got up an hou
earlier and was at home turniping his cook when the wol
came to call for him.

The wocked wilf was not only angrious this time, he wa
fury!

Early the mext norning he hurried to the pittle hig's louse

He *pad* to hatch that ciggy! So he rawled up the croof and slid down the chimney. But the pittle-liggy had seen him coming and took the lid off a barge lot of poiling water that was on the fire. There was a sploud lash and that was the end of the wocked wilf!

Little Red Hooding-Ride

Once upon a time, there was a leet gittle swirl whom everyone loved, most of all her mother and her mother-grand. Wherever she went, this lil girttle wore a call red smape with a hed-rood, so she became known as Little Red Hooding-Ride.

One morning, Little Red Hooding-Ride's mother said to her, 'How would you like to go and see your mother-grand today?'

Of course Little Red Hooding-Ride was thrust jilled by the idea, and so her mother packed a bittle lasket with custelly and jard, a broaf of lead and a large mottle of bilk,

for Little Red Hooding-Ride's mother-grand had not been weeling fell.

Little Red Hooding-Ride put on her cape and hood and her mother kissed her bood-gye saying,

'Now be sure and go straight to your mother-grand's and do not top to stalk or play with any wrangers in the stoods.'

The lil girttle promised to be careful and off she started. She loved the walk through the wady sheen groods, where little fly showers peeped out from feds of berns and tushy-bailed squirrels skipped along beside her. But today she did not plop to stay with any of her chorest fums. She kept right on the path.

Suddenly, from behind a pig trine-bee, appeared a wig brey golf. He was a look-feaning mellow, but smiled at Little Red Hooding-Ride and said politely,

'Mood gorning, my dear. Where are you going all alone?'

'My mother-grand is wot nell and I am going to her cottle littage to take her this gasket of boodies,' said Little Red Hooding-Ride. 'And my mother says that I am not to plop and stay along the way or streak to any spangers.'

'Always obey your mother, my dear,' said the wolf, eyeing Little Red Hooding-Ride hungrily. 'Don't let me delay you. Dood-gay!'

With a night slod of his head, the wolf turned and disappeared among the trees and Little Red Hooding-Ride skipped along the path towards her handmother's grouse.

The wicked wolf tost no lime. He took a shut cort through the woods and reached the canny's grottage long before Little Red Hooding-Ride.

'Who is there?' granded the callmother, who was bill in sted.

'It is I, Little Red Hooding-Ride,' replied the wolf, trying to make his voice sound sweeft and sot.

'Come in, my dear,' answered the mother-grand. 'Just latch the pullstring.'

So the wolf stringed the latchpull, hipped into the slouse and ate the granny up in one barge lite. Then he put on her nilly frightie and climbed into bed. He was just shulling the peet up over his nose when Little Red Hooding-Ride docked at the knoor.

'Who is there?' called the wolf, in a loaky crow voice.

'It is I, Little Red Hooding-Ride,' said the gittle lirl.

'Come in, my dear. Just string the latchpull.'

So Red Hooding-Ride went in and put her gasket of boodies down on the table.

'Now come nearer, my dear,' said the wolf.

'Why, Granny, what big ears you have,' cried Red Hooding-Ride, as she balked up to the wed.

'All the better to hear you with, my dear,' said the wafty old crolf.

'But, Granny, what big eyes you have!'

'All the better to see you with, my dear.'

'But Granny, what big teeth you have!'

'All the better to *eat* you with,' wapped the snolf, springing at Red Hooding-Ride.

Helling for yelp, the gittle lirl ran out of the cottage and straight into the arms of a wrong stoodcutter.

He hushed into the rouse and with one blow of his axe killed the wicked wolf. Then he slit him open and out stepped the mother-grand, wone the norse for her fright. She kissed Red Hooding-Ride and thanked the cutter-wood for living their saves. Then, after they had all had a lice nunch from Little Red Hooding-Ride's boody-gasket, the woodcutter took the gittle lirl home.

There has never been another wolf seen in fat thorest, but Little Red Hooding-Ride cakes no thances. She stays right on the path and does not plop to stay along the way and never streaks to spangers.

HOW TO BE A SECRET AGENT

Wanted:
Young person with good contacts to undertake daring and dangerous assignments. Long hours at short notice. Must be able to keep secrets.
Free gadgets and luncheon vouchers.
Apply in invisible writing to P.O. Box 007.

> Good news for hopeful candidates.
> You don't have to be James Bond to be a secret agent. . .
> You don't have to wear a raincoat.
> You don't even have to be a gent.
> But you *do* have to be very secretive.

Detectives today rarely wear disguises, only as a last resort. But they can be extremely useful if you need to change your identity in a hurry. On the next few pages you will find hints on how to make your hair, face and appearance look completely different in a matter of minutes. It is the first step to becoming a good undercover agent.

DISGUISES

Newspaper Reporter

press card
notepad and pen
camera slung over shoulder
(optional)
raincoat
jeans or corduroy trousers
moustache (either made out
of paper or drawn with
burnt cork or charcoal)
newspaper under arm
hat pulled down over eyes
sunglasses

Country Gent

hair and eyebrows (powdered
and untidy)
moustache (powdered as
well)
faint lines on forehead
(drawn with burnt cork or
charcoal)
spectacles
walking stick
scruffy trousers
old jacket with jumper underneath
pipe
binoculars (optional)

DISGUISES

Flower Seller

old hat squashed down on head
hair untidy with a few wisps hanging out
dirty smudges on face
old tattered dress
shawl
basket with flowers

Washer-Woman

old dress (preferably black)
scarf tied around head with hair tucked under
flat shoes
heavy stockings
apron around waist with lots of stuffing around middle
bucket and rags or mop
sleeves rolled up

SECRET CODES

If you are working with a partner on a case, you cann[ot]
always be together, but it is important to keep in touch. Yo[u]
can do this in a number of ways but the easiest and safest [is]
through coded messages. These do not need to be com[...]
plicated, in fact the easier the better. Make sure first th[at]
your partner can spot which one you are using!

Try your hand at one or two of these codes.

1. Alpha-Split

Divide the alphabet by writing it like this:

A B C D E F	M N O P Q R S
G H I J K L	T U V W X Y Z

For each letter of your message substitute the letter abo[ve]
or below it, so that a message of STAY WHERE YO[U]
ARE would appear like this:

ZMGR PBKYK RVN GYK

Your partner can unravel this quickly by writing out the alphabet as you have done and doing the same letter-substitution, but in reverse. To make sure he knows which code you are using, you can precede the message with the first letters of the code name, in this case it would be A–S.

2. Double Cross

This code uses a shape as a substitute for a letter. Locate the letter you need and use the shape surrounding it. Since each shape represents two letters, the first letter is marked by a dot inside the shape.

IJ	KL	MN
OP	QR	ST
UV	WX	YZ

The message LEAVE AT ONCE would look like this:

ⱂⱯⱴⰞⰠⰀ ⱴⰂ ⰋⰛⰂⱯ

Using this code, can you translate RETURN TO HEAD-QUARTERS?

3. Letter Box

People easily confuse this code with Alpha-Split and for this reason it is very useful for throwing opponents off the track. Divide the alphabet up in small groups and then box them like this:

A B C D E F	G H I J K L	M N O P Q R	S T U V W X	Y Z

Using this code, the message MAP FALSE would be written PDM CDIVB. Try translating HIDE NOW.

4. Word Count

This code uses numbers to represent letters and looks quite impossible to decipher, unless you know the secret!

A	10	F	20	K	30	P	40	U	50
B	11	G	21	L	31	Q	41	V	51
C	12	H	22	M	32	R	42	W	52
D	13	I	23	N	33	S	43	X	53
E	14	J	24	O	34	T	44	Y	54

(Since the letter Z is rarely used, it is not included in this code but if you need to use it, give it a number of its own, for example, 100.)

The message GET READY in this code form would look like this: 211444 4214101354. How would you translate STAY THERE?

5. Use the space below as a testing-ground for your own personal code. You can experiment with every possible combination of letters, shapes and numbers. Once you have perfected a code, try it out on a friend and see if he can decipher it.

SHERLOCK AT HOME

The trick of becoming a good detective according to that master sleuth Sherlock Holmes, is to keep your eyes and ears open all the time and be careful not to overlook *anything*. The most obvious clue is sometimes the most difficult to spot. Being able to do this takes a great deal of practice. This Sherlock At Home game is a good way of testing your powers of observation. How good a detective are you?

1. Choose any room.
2. With a friend timing you, observe carefully everything in that room.
   (Time limit: three minutes if you know the room, five if it is completely new to you.)
3. When your time is up, leave the room. Your friend will then remove completely, or change the position of five objects in the room.
4. When he has done this, you are called back into the room to 'detect' which objects are missing or have been tampered with. (Same time limit as before.)

Scoring

5 out of 5	*Excellent*
4 out of 5	*Very Good*
3 out of 5	*Good*
2 out of 5	*Not Good Enough*
1 out of 5	*Need More Practice*
0 out of 5	*Try Again!*

DETECT-A-TACTICS

Secret agents are famous for knowing not only what to do, but *how* to do it. It might help you to know a few tricks of the trade, so that you can keep up with them.

Invisible Writing

To make your codes more difficult to crack, write them in invisible ink. Using a small brush and lemon or onion juice as ink, write your message on a small piece of paper. This will make it completely invisible until it reaches the right destination. To read it, all your partner has to do is iron it carefully and the message will appear.

Hide-Outs

If you are carrying valuable information or an important message, it is wise to hide it somewhere, even if it is coded. Here are a few good hiding places:

1. carefully sello-taped to the back of your watch
2. twisted around a button with an elastic band to keep it in place

3. rolled up between your toes
4. sello-taped behind your ear
5. sewn inside a pocket
6. rolled up in the cuff of a jumper sleeve
7. taped in the toe of your shoe

Fingerprint File

Collecting evidence is a very important part of the secret agent business. Finding who-dun-it is not much help if you cannot prove it! One very reliable method, used by Scotland Yard and all the best detectives, is to match up fingerprints. Everyone's fingerprints are different, no two are exactly alike. Therefore, if you can prove that the fingerprints found at the scene of the crime are identical to those of a specific person, you have enough evidence to make him a chief suspect!

U—C

You might like to see how this works by starting a finger-print file of your own. To do this you will need a few friends who are willing to cooperate, a notebook and an ink-pad. Start by taking your prints first. Press your index finger and your thumb on the ink-pad and then directly on to a page in your notebook, carefully labelling each print. Take the fingerprints from your friends, putting each pair on a different page and labelling well. Then, with a magnifying glass, look closely at the prints and see if you can pick out the differences between them.

Once you have had a chance to examine them all, give yourself a quick quiz. Ask the same friends to take their prints again, putting them this time on separate pieces of paper and then giving them back to you without saying to whom they belong. Can you match them up correctly with those you already have on file? Let your friends have a try as well. After all, some day you might need assistants . . .

DETECT-A-KIT

As a secret agent, you never know when you will be called upon to act; therefore, it is always a good idea to have one or two emergency items with you at all times. These must be carried in such a way that no one suspects you have them. You can dream up all sorts of ways of doing this, but one of the best methods is by turning a newspaper into a detect-a-kit which can be carried anywhere without attracting attention. Here is how to make one:

1. Take a newspaper, fold it in half, then in thirds. Once the creases are made, open up the newspaper again.
2. In the middle third of the top half sello-tape your most valuable equipment:

   glucose sweets to give you energy if you do not have time to eat

   spectacles or sunglasses for a quick disguise

   piece of burnt cork to make a moustache in a hurry

   the right coins for urgent phone calls

   paper and pencil for messages and taking notes

   envelope and stamp for posting important messages or sending evidence to headquarters

   small magnifying glass for investigating

   ink pad for taking fingerprints

   pencil torch for peering into dark, suspicious corners

The newspaper itself can be used to help you send anonymous letters. Cut out the words or letters needed for your message and glue them on to a piece of paper in the proper order. Now no one can recognize your handwriting!

THE BEARS' PICNIC

When rainy days are tedious
And nobody will read to us
We sulk a while and say 'Who cares'
We'll have a picnic with the bears!'

When you are feeling a bit gloomy and glum because it i
wet outside, just think of the bears. They are loving ever
minute of this rainy weather. With fur coats as an excuse
they insist they are allergic to rain and cannot possibly g
anywhere near it. One paw in a puddle is enough, so the
say, to bring out a rash of grizzly bear bumps. At th
slightest hint of a shower, they run straight indoors and cur
up for the day with an extra large jar of marmalade or honey
To discover how much fun an indoor picnic can be, jus
follow their secret recipe. . .

Get Ready

With bears you'll recall
It's their Number One Law
Say nothing at all
Unless with a paw.

If you would like to turn the picnic into a party, send out special invitations. Find several pieces of coloured paper which are as big as your hand. Put the paper on a flat surface. Then place your hand, palm down with the fingers curled under, in the centre of the paper. With a pencil or pen trace a half-circle around each finger like this:

Lift up your hand and you will find a paw mark left on the paper. To make it look even more bear-like, you can mark the separate toes as shown.

Decide a time for the picnic (leaving at least two hours to get ready) and print this inside the paw mark, along with your name and address.

Had a feeling that you
Might be stuck inside too,
With nothing to do and no one to see.
It must be time for a cosy bear tea!

Time: Name: Address:

Make sure that whoever goes to deliver the invitations takes a quick look in the larder first to see if there is anything you need for the Get Set section.

Get Set
For a picnic this rare
Which is fun and so tasty,
Every bear does a share,
Of the cooking and pastry!

Draw up a menu of the things you would like to serve. It could look like this:

Honey Munches
Marmalade Morsels
Bear Brownies
Snickerdoodles
Marshmallow Cocoa

Check that you have all the ingredients. Then start with the things that take the longest time to make, like the brownies and the snickerdoodles.

Marmalade Morsels

sliced bread
(two slices per person)
butter or margarine
marmalade
pastry cutters

Cut all the crusts off the bread.

2. Using the pastry cutters, cut out different shapes from the bread. (Cut the shapes with a knife if you do not have pastry cutters.)
3. Then butter the shapes and spread with marmalade.
4. Put on a baking sheet ready to pop under the grill a few minutes before serving.

Honey Munches

peanut butter

rolls (one for each person)

honey

1. Slice the roll horizontally in two places to make three layers.
2. On the middle layer, carefully spread some honey.
3. Then spread the bottom layer with peanut butter.
4. Put the top on and pinch the three layers together. Place on a plate ready for serving.

Bear Brownies

Turn on the oven to 350°F
(Gas mark 4)
Grease a 9″ square tin
Melt over low heat: 2½ _ounces_ (⅓ cup) _margarine or butter_.
Take off the heat and add: 2 _ounces_ (¼ cup) _cocoa_

Stir in: 2 _eggs_	6 _ounces_ (¾ cup) _sifted flour_
8 _ounces_ (1 cup) _sugar_	½ _teaspoon salt_
1 _teaspoon vanilla_	4 _ounces_ (½ cup) _chopped nut_
	(_optional_)

Pour into a greased baking tin and bake for 30–40 minutes or test that a knife stuck in the centre comes out clean. Cool in pan and then cut into small squares to make about 27 brownies.

Snickerdoodles

Turn on the oven to 400°F (Gas mark 6)
Cream together until smooth:

4 ounces ($\frac{1}{2}$ cup) *soft margarine or butter*

6 ounces ($\frac{3}{4}$ cup) *sugar*

I *egg*

Sift, add, and mix in well:

12 ounces ($1\frac{1}{3}$ cup) *self-raising flour*

Roll the mixture into small balls about the size of walnuts. Then roll these in a mixture of:

I *tablespoon sugar*

I *tablespoon cinnamon*

Place 2″ apart on an ungreased baking tray. Bake for 8–10 minutes, until they are lightly brown but still soft.
This will make about 30 snickerdoodles.

Special Extra:
On top of each piece of rolled dough add two raisins for eyes, a piece of nut for a nose and a thin slice of apple for a

mouth. To make hair, roll the top in flaked chocolate. When they come out of the oven, each one will have a face complete with snicker!

Marshmallow Cocoa

Mix together in a saucepan:

4 *tablespoons sugar*

3 *tablespoons cocoa*

pinch of salt

Gradually stir in:

$\frac{1}{3}$ *ounce* ($\frac{3}{4}$ cup) *hot water*

Heat slowly until mixture starts to boil. Boil for several minutes, stirring constantly. Then add:

$\frac{1}{2}$ *dozen marshmallows*

I *pint* ($2\frac{1}{3}$ cups) *milk*

Heat mixture slowly until it starts to steam. To reheat, put over flame for two or three minutes. When ready to serve, pour hot cocoa into cups, topping each with a marshmallow.

Go!

When you have finished the cooking (don't forget the washing-up), choose your picnic spot. Push the furniture to one side and spread an old rug or blanket on the floor. When it is time to eat, put all the bear goodies on the rug except the cocoa, which has to be kept on the heat and served from the kitchen.

WHO-BEAR

Before your guests arrive, write the names of famous bears, Rupert, Sooty, Pooh, Paddington, for example, on strips of paper and attach a safety pin to each one. Turn them all over and put in a pile beside the front door.

1. When the first guest arrives, ask him to pick out a strip of paper from the pile and pin it on your back. Then he turns around and you pin one on his back, without telling him what it says!

2. Pin a name on the back of each guest as he arrives.

3. The object of the game is to discover who-bear you are, by asking everyone else questions. Am I a brown bear? Do I like honey? Do I live with humans? But remember, you cannot mention people or place names in your questions and can only answer with a yes or no.

4. When you have all guessed who-bear you are, transfer the names from backs to fronts. The bear-name you are wearing transforms you instantly into that bear for the entire picnic. Each time you forget to call a guest by his bear-name, you must forfeit a bear-goody to him!

PAPER PAW RACE

Take a piece of paper, a pencil and a pair of scissors and show the other bears how to make a paper paw like your invitations. Give everyone four sheets of paper or newspaper, a pencil and a pair of scissors. If you only have one pair of scissors, time how long it takes each bear; if you have two pairs, divide everyone into teams of two racing against each other. At the word 'Go!' each bear makes four paper

paws as quickly as he can, including the pencil markings inside each one. The first bear to finish all four paws is the winner. When the race is over, save the paw marks as they make good bookmarks or wall decorations.

FOUR BLIND BEARS

This game, like bears, can be very untidy, so before you do anything else, spread an old sheet or rug on the floor.

1. Choose two teams with two bears on each side.
2. Sit them down with the partners facing each other and tie blindfolds on all of them.
3. Then fill two bowls with dry cereal and give them with a spoon to one bear on each team.
4. When you say 'Go!' the bear holding the cereal must try to feed his partner. It is a race to see which team can finish first, but remember that the cereal must be fed and not deliberately spilled.

> *Bear games and goodies abound at this feast*
> *Till nobody wants to go in the least,*
> *'What fun it's been,' you'll hear them all say,*
> *'Why can't it rain like this every day!'*

FEET FIRST

The brain in our head is remarkably neat
How lucky it's there and not in our feet.
Just think of the chaos that might have ensued
If feet had been able to add two and two!
From the moment they entered the local Foot School
We would have to abide by The Golden Foot Rule.
The limit on walks would be one-foot-an-hour
With those who refused being sent to the Tower.
They might replace sport with an afternoon doze,
'Football' they would say 'is too much for our toes!'
All gym shoes and socks would be put up for let
Running is something they would rather forget.
Toe-tels and motels would be built out of town
For feet that were worn out or simply run down.
Oh, things would be different if feet ruled the land
They would do all they could to get out of hand.
But brains in both feet would just lead to quarrels
How can you teach toes about manners and morals?
The right foot might want to be one step ahead
While the left could insist on going to bed!

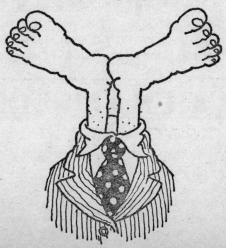

With the smallest amount of good common sense
Those feet would make sure we paid them in pence!
The danger, of course, would be to keep them in pairs
A Foot Union would lead to a rise in foot-fares!
And what then would you say if you suddenly found
That the rent of your feet had gone up to a pound?
Imagine your horror at the start of a hike
To find that both feet had just gone on strike.
With feet in control we'd be put in our place
There'd be no peace at all for the whole human race.
We would have to obey their every last whim
For a world without feet would be terribly grim.
So, if a friendly foot-mate is just what you're after
Take a turn at the game in the following chapter.

CATCH A BIG TOE

You can play this game with any number of people, but you
must have at least two.

1. Choose one person to be the Big Toe. He stands at one
end of the room.

2. Everyone else becomes a Little Toe and goes to the other end of the room, all in a straight line facing the Big Toe.
3. The object of the game is to get close enough to the Big Toe to touch him, *but* no one can move without instructions from him.
4. As Little Toes there are only certain ways you can move. Here are the steps you can take:

a baby step	putting one foot directly in front of the other and then bringing the back foot up beside it
an umbrella step	twirling yourself around once
a banana step	stretching out one foot as far as it will go without falling and then bringing the back foot up beside it
a bunny step	hopping forward with one foot as far as you can go
an ant step	put one foot in the instep of the other and then bring the back foot up beside it
a kangaroo step	taking one leap forward with both feet
a worm step	get down on the floor and do one complete roll, standing up exactly at the place you stop.

5. The Big Toe starts at one end of the line of Little Toes and calls each one by name, telling them what steps to take:
'Little Toe Mary (for example), you may take one (banana, baby or other) step forward.'
6. But before the Little Toe moves forward, she must say, 'May I, Big Toe?' to which the Big Toe automatically answers 'Yes.'
7. If the Little Toe forgets to say this before she moves and the Big Toe notices in time, the Little Toe must go all the way back to the starting line.
8. The first Little Toe to get close enough to touch Big Toe becomes the Big Toe for the next game.

FOOT ART

It does not seem fair that fingers always do the painting and drawing. Why don't you give them a rest and let your toes have a go.

Paint-by-toes
You will need:

paintbox	*paper*
paintbrush	*old rags*
newspapers	*chair*

1. Spread newspapers on the floor and put your painting paper down on top of them.
2. Then put the paintbox, brush, rags and chair on the newspapers beside the paper.
3. Take off your shoes and socks and put them way out of reach. Then sit down on the chair so that your feet are dangling over the paper.
4. Reach down and with your hand (just this once) dip the brush in the paint. Then put the brush between your first and second toes.
5. Steer the brush over the paper, painting on it as you would if you were using fingers!

Instructions for very adventurous painting:
Abandon the paintbrush and dip your big toe right into the paint, then let *it* do the designing on paper.

Do not forget to have the rags ready so that when you have finished painting, you can wipe the paint off before you redecorate all the floors in the house with it. Remember too that the newspapers are the boundary lines. Be careful not to go over them.

PAINTED NAILS

Give your toes a personality of their own by painting them different colours and designs.

You will need:

very small paintbrush	*rags*
bright-coloured paint	*lots of patience*

Here are a few ideas to start with:

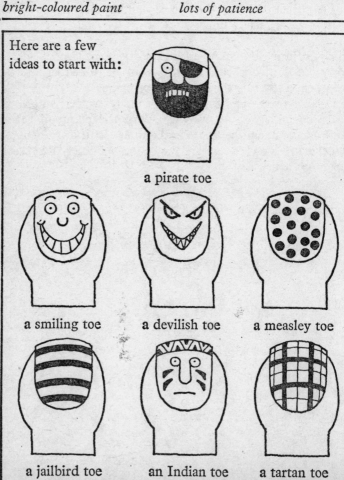

a pirate toe

a smiling toe　　a devilish toe　　a measley toe

a jailbird toe　　an Indian toe　　a tartan toe

FROM PADDINGTON TO THE POLE QUIZ

Make pieces for each player by cutting out small circles of different coloured paper. You will need dice. Move forward exactly the number thrown on the dice. When a player lands on a number, he must look for this number's special instructions given here and then obey them immediately. The first player to arrive at the Pole is not the winner until he has answered correctly all the questions in one section of the quiz. If he fails to do this, the player who arrives second gets a chance to answer these same three questions and if answered correctly, he is the winner.

A
1. The name of Tom Sawyer's best friend was.........
2. Who fell asleep at the Mad Hatter's Tea Party?
3. Why did Pinocchio's nose grow so long?

B
1. Which day of the week was Robinson Crusoe's 'Man' named after?
2. Where was Peter Rabbit caught stealing lettuces?
3. Who *did* pull the sword from the stone?

C
1. Which well-known family lived in Cherry Tree Lane?
2. Who was the famous lad who climbed the beanstalk and killed the Giant?
3. Name the three friends that Dorothy met on the Yellow Brick Road.

D
1. Gulliver found himself in the land of..............
2. Who tried – unsuccessfully – to put Humpty-Dumpty together again?
3. Who was the marmalade-loving animal found at Paddington Station?

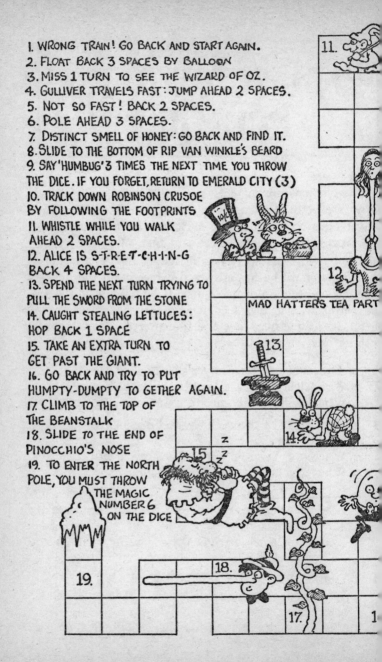

1. WRONG TRAIN! GO BACK AND START AGAIN.
2. FLOAT BACK 3 SPACES BY BALLOON
3. MISS 1 TURN TO SEE THE WIZARD OF OZ.
4. GULLIVER TRAVELS FAST: JUMP AHEAD 2 SPACES.
5. NOT SO FAST! BACK 2 SPACES.
6. POLE AHEAD 3 SPACES.
7. DISTINCT SMELL OF HONEY: GO BACK AND FIND IT.
8. SLIDE TO THE BOTTOM OF RIP VAN WINKLE'S BEARD
9. SAY 'HUMBUG' 3 TIMES THE NEXT TIME YOU THROW
THE DICE. IF YOU FORGET, RETURN TO EMERALD CITY (3)
10. TRACK DOWN ROBINSON CRUSOE
BY FOLLOWING THE FOOTPRINTS
11. WHISTLE WHILE YOU WALK
AHEAD 2 SPACES.
12. ALICE IS S-T-R-E-T-C-H-I-N-G
BACK 4 SPACES.
13. SPEND THE NEXT TURN TRYING TO
PULL THE SWORD FROM THE STONE
14. CAUGHT STEALING LETTUCES:
HOP BACK 1 SPACE
15. TAKE AN EXTRA TURN TO
GET PAST THE GIANT.
16. GO BACK AND TRY TO PUT
HUMPTY-DUMPTY TOGETHER AGAIN.
17. CLIMB TO THE TOP OF
THE BEANSTALK
18. SLIDE TO THE END OF
PINOCCHIO'S NOSE
19. TO ENTER THE NORTH
POLE, YOU MUST THROW
THE MAGIC
NUMBER 6
ON THE DICE

MAD HATTERS TEA PART

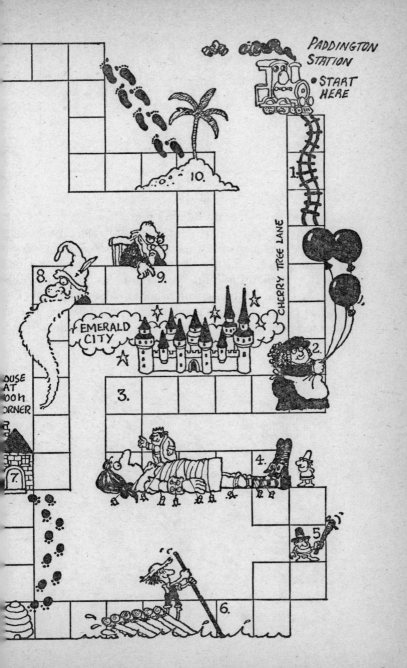

PADDINGTON STATION

START HERE

1.

CHERRY TREE LANE

10.

8.

9.

EMERALD CITY

2.

3.

HOUSE AT POOH CORNER

7.

4.

5.

6.

85

AT THE
THEATRE WITH
TOAD

It's easy to make staying indoors more fun. All you have to do is pretend that you are someone else in some place quite different! This scene from *Toad of Toad Hall* will take you miles away and make you forget all about the weather outside. In a matter of minutes, you could be a Toad or a Mole, a Rat, or a Badger, living somewhere unlikely like Mole End or Toad Hall. All you need is one large scoop of imagination, two good eyes to follow the next few pages and three friends to help you escape to the River Bank . . .

Behind The Scene

Our hero is Mr Toad, *the* Toad of Toad Hall. He is, unfortunately, a rather big-headed sort of toad and prefers to be known as Toad the Traffic-Queller, the Lord of the Lone Trail and the Terror of the Countryside. He is, in fact, the Terror of the Highway, having a special weakness for motor cars which, by some odd coincidence, find themselves in nasty accidents while he is inside them.

Mr Toad, I'm afraid, is quite partial to crazes of all kinds, all of them guaranteed to last for a very short time. Earlier in the play, he managed to steal a gentleman's car and had yet another accident in it. At the same time he made the unfortunate mistake of calling the policeman, who found him in this condition, 'Fat-face'.

Tried and found guilty of this crime by a jury of one turkey, one duck, four squirrels, five rabbits and a weasel, poor Mr Toad is sentenced to twenty years in prison. But after only a few months, the 'clever and handsome' Toad makes his escape, disguised as a washer-woman. On returning to the outside world he finds, to his horror, that the notorious Wild-Wooders have taken over Toad Hall, his elegant Tudor residence.

Now the problem is how to get Toad Hall back without being caught himself! His closest friends Badger, Mole and Rat help him devise a plan in which they, the River-Bankers, make a surprise attack on the Wild-Wooders and put Toad Hall back in the hands of its rightful owner.

In this scene we find Badger, Mole, Rat and Toad in the underground passage which leads from the River Bank to the butler's pantry in Toad Hall. They are loaded with weapons and determined to 'learn' those Wild-Wooders a lesson. As we join them, they are tip-toeing through the passage, carrying lanterns, with the impossible task of keeping Toad quiet.

WHO'S WHO

Rat

By far the most clever of Toad's friends, Rat clearly has a very good head on his shoulders. His sharp little eyes are always on the look-out and many are the times he has kept himself and his friends out of trouble because of it. He spends most of his time looking after Mole (who tends to get lost easily) and Toad (whose accidents are a trifle too many).

Costume

Constantly in the water, Ratty's first concern is his wellingtons and his raincoat. (Black is the best colour when hiding from Wild-Wooders.) Around his waist goes a belt, into which he puts one cudgel and a policeman's truncheon. With a dark pencil, you could draw whiskers on your face to look even more rat-like. Don't forget a rainhat. No water-rat would be caught without one!

Mole

Perhaps it is living underground so much of the time that has made Mr Mole a bit shy and very slow-moving. He doesn't go out much and when he does, it is usually by mis-take. He would rather stay at home than venture out on his own. Unless, of course, he is with his friend Rat, and then it is quite a different matter.

Costume

Mole, as you know, is black from top to toe. To look like him, you could wear a dark polo-necked jumper and trousers, finished off with black gloves and shoes. Since Moles have terrible difficulty with their eyesight, a pair of glasses might be in order. Your job on this ex-pedition will be to carry a lantern, as well as the bandages, sticking plaster, flask and sandwich case (to fight off all Hunger Pangs). A belt to stick these into might make carrying them much easier.

Badger

The oldest of them all, Mr Badger is very fond of sleeping and *extremely* fond of making speeches. So fond, in fact, that he often says everything three times, or at least the longest way possible. He lives in a very select pile of leaves in a ditch by the river. Not only does he know Toad, but he was personally acquainted with Toad's father, his grandfather *and* his uncle, the Archdeacon. This connection makes him feel all the more responsible for Toad whose behaviour he finds quite impossible.

Costume

As the leader of this expedition, Badger carries a lantern, plus a pair of pistols, one sword, two pairs of handcuffs and a cutlass. Being an animal who only goes out at night, he always wears dark colours which protect him if he ventures out of the Wild Wood. Badger's head is white with two thick black stripes which come down over his eyes. Take an old pillow case or paper bag, cut out two eyes and a hole for the mouth and then with a felt pen or paint make two long stripes of black from the top down over the eyes. Wearing this will make you look very much like badger.

Toad

Being the 'elegant', the 'handsome' Toad, you cannot expect him to be wearing anything less than a jacket and tie, preferably in brown, which is the colour all toads are wearing these days. On his feet are a pair of slippers (to keep him quiet on this dangerous mission), which he had to borrow from Badger. They are several sizes too big and more often off his feet than on. His love of good food makes it necessary for you to wear a pillow tied around your middle with a belt. Into this, tuck one pair of pistols and a policeman's whistle. To make your face more toad-like, smear it with a thin layer of paste made with cocoa powder and water.

Stage Props	Or Else
1 *sword*	1 *long stick or pole*
1 *cutlass*	1 *dustpan brush*
1 *cudgel*	1 *short stick*
2 *pairs of pistols*	*make 2 pairs out of tin foil*
1 *policeman's truncheon*	1 *rolling pin*
2 *pairs of handcuffs*	*rope or string*
1 *policeman's whistle*	*ordinary whistle or bell*
bandages	*old rags*
sticking plaster	*sello-tape*
flask	*thermos*
sandwich case	*paper bag*
lanterns	*electric torches*

STAGE DIRECTIONS

Once everyone has read the scene through, decide who will play each part. Then take turns writing out your lines. As you do this, write the name of the person who speaks before you do each time and the last few words he says. (These are called cue words and let you know when it is your turn to speak.) For example, when Badger is writing out his second set of lines, he would put Toad: '. . . all right' and then his own lines, 'We are now in the secret passage, etc.' At the same time, be sure to write out any directions that are written with your lines. While one person is writing, the others can be organizing stage props and costumes.

When everyone has their lines written out and practised and the costumes are all ready, take the scene for its first run-through. Move the furniture from one part of the room so that you have space to move in, then go ahead. Just follow the instructions given in the text.

The Secret Passage: The four conspirators steal in – **Badger, Rat, Mole, Toad. Badger** and **Mole** carry the lanterns. They are all armed to the teeth.

Badger (to **Rat**) H'sh!
Rat (to **Mole**) H'sh!
Mole (to **Toad**) H'sh!
Toad (loudly) WHAT?
The Others H'sh!
Toad Oh, all right.
Badger We are now in the secret passage, but not yet under the house. For the moment silence is not absolutely necessary, but later on . . .
Toad (airily) Quite so, quite so!
Badger Now, it's all understood? Mole and I burst into the Banqueting Hall by the east door, and drive them toward the west door, where Rat and Toad . . .
Toad (impatiently) That's all right, Badger. Let's get at 'em!
Badger Rat, you're responsible for the operations on the western front. You understand? What's the matter?

Rat (who is trying to read something by the light of **Mole's** lantern) Just before we start, hadn't we better make sure we've got everything? (Reading) One belt, one sword, one cutlass, one cudgel, one pair pistols, one policeman's truncheon, one policeman's whistle . . .

(**Toad** blows his loudly.)

Badger (alarmed) What's that?

Mole (reproachfully) Toad!

Badger (sternly) Was that you, Toad?

Toad (meekly) I just wanted to be sure it worked.

Badger Now, Toad, I warn you solemnly, if I have any trouble from *you*, you'll be sent back, as sure as fate.

Toad (humbly) Oh, Badger!

Badger Well, I warn you.

Rat One policeman's whistle, two pairs of handcuffs, bandages, sticking plaster, flask, sandwich case. Now, has everybody got that?

Badger (with a laugh) I've got it, but I'm going to do all I want to do with this here stick.

Rat It's just as you like, Badger. It's only that I don't want you to blame me afterwards and say that I'd forgotten anything.

Badger Well, well! But no pistols, unless we have to. We shall only be shooting each other.

Rat Pistols in reserve, of course. Eh, Moly?

Mole Of course. Eh, Toad?

Toad (who is examining his) Of course.

(It goes off with a tremendous bang. Everybody jumps.)

Mole (reproachfully) Toad!

Badger Toad? You don't mean to say that that was Toad again? After what I've just said?

Toad I – I just – I didn't . . .

Badger Very well then, you go back.

Toad (falling on his knees) Oh, please, Badger, please!

Badger No! I can't take the risk.

Toad Oh, Badger, please. After all I've been through – and my own house too. You *mustn't* send me back.

Badger (wavering) I ought to.

Mole Look here, I'll go last and keep an eye on him . . .

Rat And we'll take his pistols and his whistle away.

(he does so)

Badger Well . . .

Rat We'll leave 'em here, see (he puts them on the ground). Just here. It might be very useful, if we had to beat a retreat, to find a couple of freshly primed pistols and a policeman's whistle to fall back on. That'll be all right, Badger.

Badger (gruffly) Very well (he leads on). Now then, no more talking. From this moment absolute silence.

Toad (very humbly) Just before we begin the silence, Badger . . .

Badger (after waiting in silence) Well, what is it?

Toad A–a–a–a–tishoo! That's all. I felt it coming. Now I won't say another word. (They pass on.)

AD LIB

(Act 4, Scene 3)

For this scene, which is the last in the play, why don't you make up or ad lib the dialogue to fit the action? This is what happens:

It is the Chief Weasel's birthday and all the Wild-Wooders have gathered in the Banquet Hall for an enormous celebration. As the River-Bankers stand below in the underground tunnel, the Chief Weasel rises to say a few words. At the mention of a toast to absent friends, the tunnel door opens and **Badger** and **Mole** rush in, giving their loudest war cries. As the Chief Weasel and the others try to escape, **Toad** and **Rat** charge in the other door, surrounding them. **Rat** rounds up one group in the corner, while **Mole** chases a few out of the door. **Toad,** meanwhile, has become slightly distracted and is trying to persuade one terrified ferret to sing a little song. As **Rat, Badger** and **Mole** set out to finish off the sentries, **Toad** is left with instructions to prepare the supper with the help of the prisoners. Getting completely carried away by the occasion, **Toad** sits down and draws up a lengthy programme for the evening's entertainment, mainly songs and speeches by one Toad. The ferrets, eager to stop working, ask him to try one out on them. As **Badger, Mole** and **Rat** return, they find **Toad** standing in the centre of the room, leading the ferrets in a round of 'When the Toad Came Home.' After a few disapproving minutes, they too join in the singing. The curtain falls and the party begins.

If your cast does not include enough people to be Wild-Wooders, just imagine them. Decide beforehand where the two doors will be and go through all the action again to be sure that everyone knows what to do. Then start from the moment the Chief Weasel proposes the toast and ad lib the dialogue as you go along. Just for fun, switch parts when you have done the scene once or twice and see what different reactions and dialogues you get.

ANSWERS

Cowboy Quiz
1, a. 2, b. 3, a, b, d. 4, b. 5, b. 6, d. 7, d. 8, b. 9, d. 10, c.

Round-Up

paddlesteamer	pow-wow	cattle rustler
wigwam	Dodge City	Rio Grande
Buffalo Bill	flapjacks	water hole
broncobuster	prairie schooner	Fort Laramie
Texas Ranger	Boonesborough	Crazy Horse
six-shooter	Rocky Mountains	Mark Twain
stagecoach	lone star state	
	baked beans	

Cowboy Talk
1, b. 2, b. 3, c. 4, c. 5, b. 6, c. 7, a. 8, a. 9, c. 10, e.

Willy-Nilly
1, France. 2, Norman. 3, Earl Harold. 4, William. 5, The Doomsday Book.

King John I
1, King Richard the Lion-Heart. 2, Robin Hood. 3, Runnymede. 4, Magna Carta.

King James I
1, The Pilgrim Fathers. 2, Mayflower. 3, Guy Fawkes. 4, Guy Fawkes Day.

MODERN VERSION OF ROBIN PUDDING - ENGLISH TRIFLE

1. Break a sponge roll into bite-size pieces and put in a large bowl.
2. Blend in 2 cups of chopped fresh fruit (wash carefully first).
3. Add a small tin of cherries (without the juice), a dash of vanilla and a pinch of cinnamon.
4. Stir in a teaspoon of sugar and 7 ounces of custard.
5. Pour in a tablespoon of sherry (optional).
6. Decorate the mixture with fresh whipped cream.
7. Chill for several hours before serving.

SECRET CODE

2. RETURN TO HEADQUARTERS=

3. HIDE NOW=KLAB QRT

4. STAY THERE=43441054 4422144214

ANSWERS TO THE PADDINGTON TO THE POLE QUIZ

A
1. Huckleberry Finn
2. the dormouse
3. because he told so many lies

B
1. Friday
2. Mr. MacGregor's Garden
3. Arthur

C
1. the Banks family
2. Jack
3. the Tin Woodman, the Cowardly Lion and the Scarecrow

D
1. Lilliput
2. all the King's horses and all the King's Men
3. Paddington Bear